BARTÓK *for* TRUMPET

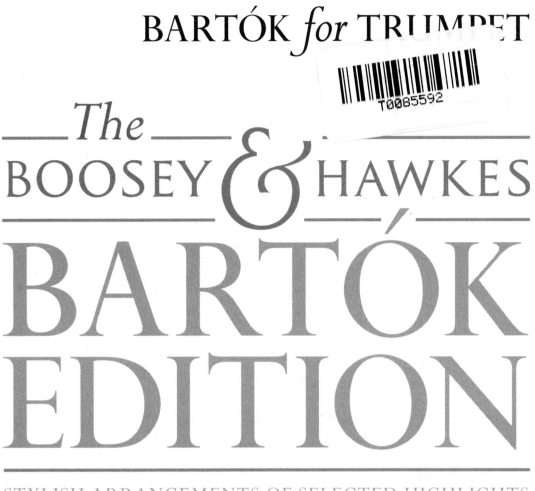

The
BOOSEY & HAWKES
BARTÓK
EDITION

STYLISH ARRANGEMENTS OF SELECTED HIGHLIGHTS
FROM THE LEADING 20TH CENTURY COMPOSER

Selected and arranged by Hywel Davies

BOOSEY & HAWKES

Boosey & Hawkes Music Publishers Ltd
www.boosey.com

HYWEL DAVIES

Hywel Davies is an award-winning composer, arranger and creative artist.

His compositions have been performed by a wealth of ensembles including Kokoro (Bournemouth Symphony Orchestra's new music ensemble, with whom he has a long-standing association), and have been broadcast internationally by the BBC, CBC (Canada) and ABC (Australia). In 2003 he was the recipient of an Arts Council England International Fellowship.

As an arranger, Davies has been published by Boosey & Hawkes, Durand-Salabert-Eschig, Chester Music, Novello, the Associated Board of the Royal Schools of Music and Music Sales. Recent projects for Boosey & Hawkes have included two volumes of pieces by Ástor Piazzolla (*El viaje* & *Vuelvo al sur*), and a volume of works by Rachmaninoff (*Play Rachmaninoff*); he has also compiled several anthologies of piano music including most recently *American Greats* and *Ballet & Other Dances* from the *Boosey & Hawkes Solo Piano Collection*.

Davies is in demand as a sonic and installation artist, and has received commissions from organisations including Arts Council England and the National Trust, often working as an Artist in Residence.

www.hyweldavies.co.uk

Published by Boosey & Hawkes Music Publishers Ltd
Aldwych House
71–91 Aldwych
London
WC2B 4HN

www.boosey.com

© Copyright 2016 by Boosey & Hawkes Music Publishers Ltd

ISMN 979-0-060-13070-0
ISBN 978-1-78454-146-0

First impression 2016

Printed by Halstan:
Halstan UK, 2-10 Plantation Road, Amersham, Bucks, HP6 6HJ. United Kingdom
Halstan DE, Weißliliengasse 4, 55116 Mainz. Germany

With thanks to Richard Colquhoun for advice
Cover design by Chloë Alexander Design (chloealexanderdesign.dphoto.com)
Trumpet performance by John Shaddock
Piano performance, audio recording, mixing and mastering by Robin Bigwood

BARTÓK *for* TRUMPET

Selected and arranged by Hywel Davies

Piano Accompaniment

FULL PERFORMANCE & BACKING TRACK CD

The enclosed CD contains demonstration and piano accompaniment backing tracks for all pieces in this book.

 Track 01 is a tuning note. Ensure you are in tune with this before using the rest of the CD.

 Demonstration tracks are included for all pieces. Track numbers are shown in black circles.

 Backing tracks are included for all pieces. Track numbers are shown in grey circles.

BÉLA BARTÓK

Béla Bartók was born in the Hungarian town of Nagyszentmiklós (now Sînnicolau Mare in Romania) on 25 March 1881, and received his first music lessons from his mother. When his family moved he took further lessons in Pressburg (now Bratislava in Slovakia) before becoming a student at the Royal Academy of Music in Budapest – graduating in 1903. He began to establish an international reputation as a fine pianist, and was soon drawn into teaching: in 1907 he became professor of piano at the Academy.

Bartók's earliest compositions offer a blend of late Romanticism and nationalist elements, formed under the influences of Wagner, Brahms, Liszt and Strauss. Around 1905 his friend and fellow-composer Zoltán Kodály directed his attention to Hungarian folk music and – coupled with his discovery of the music of Debussy – Bartók's musical language changed dramatically. As he absorbed more and more of the spirit of Hungarian folk songs and dances, his own music grew more concentrated, chromatic and dissonant. Although a sense of key is sometimes lost in individual passages, Bartók never espoused atonality as a compositional technique.

Bartók's interest in folk music was not merely passive: he was an assiduous ethnomusicologist, and undertook his first systematic collecting trips in Hungary with Kodály. Thereafter Bartók's interest and involvement grew deeper and his scope wider, encompassing a number of ethnic traditions both near at hand and further afield: Transylvanian, Romanian, North African and others.

In the 1920s and '30s Bartók's international fame spread, and he toured widely, both as pianist (usually in his own works) and as a respected composer. Works like *Dance Suite* for orchestra (1923) and *Divertimento* for strings (1939) maintained his high profile. He continued to teach at the Academy of Music until his resignation in 1934, devoting much of his free time thereafter to his ethnomusicological research.

With the outbreak of the Second World War, and despite his deep attachment to his homeland, life in Hungary became intolerable and Bartók emigrated to the United States. Here his material conditions worsened considerably, despite initial promise: although he obtained a post at Columbia University and was able to pursue his folk-music studies, his concert engagements become very much rarer. He received few commissions, so the request for a Concerto for Orchestra (1943) was therefore particularly important, bringing him much-needed income. Bartók died following a period of ill health on 26 September 1945.

COME HOME, LIDI

For Children – book I, no 3

BÉLA BARTÓK
(1881–1945)

For Children (1908–1909, and later revised) is a two-volume collection of folk song transcriptions and arrangements which Bartók created for piano teaching. Volume I contains songs of Hungarian origin, whilst the music in volume II is Slovakian. The words of this Hungarian song are translated: *"I've lost my mate, my pretty marriageable daughter. Come home, my daughter called Lidi."*

BAKING SONG

For Children – book I, no 1

BÉLA BARTÓK
(1881–1945)

The words of this Hungarian piece are translated, *'Let's bake something made of flour with filling – a snail-shaped strudel, round and sweet!'*

poco rit

ROGUE'S SONG / SORROW

For Children – book II, no 7

BÉLA BARTÓK
(1881–1945)

This Slovakian song tells the story of a soldier (the 'rogue') who is witnessed committing a heinous crime after returning from war in Poland. He is sentenced to death but his life is spared: *'The sheriff wanted to hang me, but there were girls there who did not allow it.'*

ROUND DANCE

For Children – book I, no 17

BÉLA BARTÓK
(1881–1945)

A serene melody over a swaying piano accompaniment. The text of the Hungarian folk song is translated: *"My lovely girl is dressed in white; turn to me, you married bride."*

SONG OF THE RAKE

Mikrokosmos – no 65

BÉLA BARTÓK
(1881–1945)

Mikrokosmos (1926–1939) is a collection of 153 pieces which Bartók wrote for students to assist them in navigating their way through some of the most important technical and musical problems faced by developing pianists. It is considered one of the most significant pedagogical works for piano written in the twentieth century. This is a folk melody in Dorian mode on G. The text is translated, *"Could you, would you let me share your rake so fine?" "No sir, go sir, don't you know this rake is mine?" "I would trade you apples from my tree." "Never! My fine rake is just for me!"*

CAROL № 7

Romanian Christmas Carols – set II, no 7

BÉLA BARTÓK
(1881–1945)

The twenty original songs collected by Bartók (published in two volumes in 1915) would have been sung by young Romanian carol singers on Christmas Eve. Many of the texts are based on Christian liturgy; some are of a pagan origin. The original Romanian text of the seventh carol in set II is translated *'At the quiet well-spring the Lord God and the Virgin Mary and a small Son were resting.'* The figure in bar 12 may be played by either trumpet or piano.

ON THE STREET IN ISTVÁND

For Children – book I, no 15

BÉLA BARTÓK
(1881–1945)

Melody with syncopated piano accompaniment. The Hungarian text is translated: *'I walk past the house of my beloved on the street in Istvánd, but she is still far away from me.'*

LAMENT

For Children – book II, no 28

BÉLA BARTÓK
(1881–1945)

A melody over sustained piano chords and broken chords. The Slovakian text is translated: *"I have wandered many nights on bumpy, cold and muddy roads; but I never minded them..."*

THE BANKS OF THE DANUBE

For Children – book II, no 33

BÉLA BARTÓK
(1881–1945)

A delicate song of parting about a soldier leaving his lover and home: 'The Dabube's bank is green at Bratislava'.

SASH DANCE

Romanian Folk Dances – no 2

BÉLA BARTÓK
(1881–1945)

The Romanian Folk Dances were written in 1915. Originally a melody for flute, this delicate circle dance for girls is in Dorian mode on C. The editorial tempo markings reflect the undulating feel commonly featured in performances of this piece.

THE TWO ROSES

For Children – book II, no 3

BÉLA BARTÓK
(1881–1945)

The text of this Slovakian song is translated: *"That girl gave me one of two roses by the tree." "Give me the other one, because it means love." "I won't give it, because there'll be none left for me!"* Approach this teasing piece playfully.

WHERE ARE YOUR GEESE?

For Children – book II, no 13

BÉLA BARTÓK
(1881–1945)

This piece is written in a mixture of Dorian and Aeolian modes on C. The text is translated: *"I went into the water to fetch the straying geese, and my shirt got wet; when I go to see my sweetheart it will be better."*

poco allargando

COUNTY FAIR

Mikrokosmos – no 47

BÉLA BARTÓK
(1881–1945)

Written in the Dorian mode on F, this is a lively and boisterous piece. Bartók's original metronome mark is shown, but this piece may be played as effectively at a slower tempo as indicated by the additional editorial tempo marking.

BARTÓK *for* TRUMPET

The
BOOSEY & HAWKES
BARTÓK
EDITION

STYLISH ARRANGEMENTS OF SELECTED HIGHLIGHTS
FROM THE LEADING 20TH CENTURY COMPOSER

Selected and arranged by Hywel Davies

TRUMPET IN B♭

BOOSEY & HAWKES

Boosey & Hawkes Music Publishers Ltd
www.boosey.com

Published by Boosey & Hawkes Music Publishers Ltd
Aldwych House
71–91 Aldwych
London
WC2B 4HN

www.boosey.com

ISMN 979-0-060-13070-0
ISBN 978-1-78454-146-0

First impression 2016

Printed by Halstan:
Halstan UK, 2-10 Plantation Road, Amersham, Bucks, HP6 6HJ. United Kingdom
Halstan DE, Weißliliengasse 4, 55116 Mainz. Germany

With thanks to Richard Colquhoun for advice
Cover design by Chloë Alexander Design (chloealexanderdesign.dphoto.com)
Trumpet performance by John Shaddock
Piano performance, audio recording, mixing and mastering by Robin Bigwood

BARTÓK *for* TRUMPET

Selected and arranged by Hywel Davies

Trumpet in B♭

FULL PERFORMANCE & BACKING TRACK CD

The enclosed CD contains demonstration and piano accompaniment backing tracks for all pieces in this book.

 Track 01 is a tuning note. Ensure you are in tune with this before using the rest of the CD.

Demonstration tracks are included for all pieces. Track numbers are shown in black circles.

 Backing tracks are included for all pieces. Track numbers are shown in grey circles.

COME HOME, LIDI

For Children – book I, no 3

BÉLA BARTÓK
(1881–1945)

BAKING SONG

For Children – book I, no 1

BÉLA BARTÓK
(1881–1945)

ROGUE'S SONG / SORROW

For Children – book II, no 7

BÉLA BARTÓK
(1881–1945)

ROUND DANCE

For Children – book I, no 17

BÉLA BARTÓK
(1881–1945)

SONG OF THE RAKE

Mikrokosmos – no 65

BÉLA BARTÓK
(1881–1945)

CAROL № 7

Romanian Christmas Carols – set II, no 7

BÉLA BARTÓK
(1881–1945)

ON THE STREET IN ISTVÁND

For Children – book I, no 15

BÉLA BARTÓK
(1881–1945)

LAMENT

For Children – book II, no 28

BÉLA BARTÓK
(1881–1945)

THE BANKS OF THE DANUBE

For Children – book II, no 33

BÉLA BARTÓK
(1881–1945)

SASH DANCE

Romanian Folk Dances – no 2

BÉLA BARTÓK
(1881–1945)

THE TWO ROSES

For Children – book II, no 3

BÉLA BARTÓK
(1881–1945)

WHERE ARE YOUR GEESE?

For Children – book II, no 13

BÉLA BARTÓK
(1881–1945)

COUNTY FAIR

Mikrokosmos – no 47

BÉLA BARTÓK
(1881–1945)

IN YUGOSLAV STYLE

Mikrokosmos – no 40

BÉLA BARTÓK
(1881–1945)

Allegretto ♩ = 120

MY LOVER'S MOTHER

For Children – book II, no 12

BÉLA BARTÓK
(1881–1945)

Andante rubato ♩ = c84

PLOUGHING

For Children – book II, no 14

BÉLA BARTÓK
(1881–1945)

Moderato ♩ = 84   **Più mosso** ♩ = 108

TEASING SONG

For Children, book II, no 18

BÉLA BARTÓK
(1881–1945)

THE LOST COUPLE

For Children – book I, no 11

TAVERN SONG

For Children, book I, no 21

BÉLA BARTÓK
(1881–1945)

CANON

For Children – book II, no 29

BÉLA BARTÓK
(1881–1945)

JEERING SONG

For Children – book I, no 30

BÉLA BARTÓK
(1881–1945)

SWINE-HERD'S SONG

For Children – book I, no 37

BÉLA BARTÓK
(1881–1945)

BULGARIAN RHYTHM

Mikrokosmos – no 113

BÉLA BARTÓK
(1881–1945)

STICK DANCE

Romanian Folk Dances – no 1

BÉLA BARTÓK
(1881–1945)

IN YUGOSLAV STYLE

Mikrokosmos – no 40

BÉLA BARTÓK
(1881–1945)

This piece presents an imitation of Yugoslovian bagpipe music in mixolydian mode on B♭, where the piano accompaniment imitates a drone and the trumpet carries a chanter-like melody.

MY LOVER'S MOTHER

For Children – book II, no 12

BÉLA BARTÓK
(1881–1945)

A Slovakian song whose words are translated: *"Mother of my lover, whichever way I go, don't curse my path."*

PLOUGHING

For Children – book II, no 14

BÉLA BARTÓK
(1881–1945)

This Slovakian song is translated: *'On a pine-topped hill there are six oxen. Four are ploughing, two are harrowing; who is driving them?'*

TEASING SONG

For Children, book II, no 18

BÉLA BARTÓK
(1881–1945)

The text of this Slovakian text is translated: *'Once I was your love, now I am your comrade, but who cares? If I go out to the street I will find an ape better than you; I don't need you!'*

THE LOST COUPLE

For Children – book I, no 11

BÉLA BARTÓK
(1881–1945)

This folk song shares the same text as used in *Come Home, Lidi* on page 2.

Più sostenuto

TAVERN SONG

For Children, book I, no 21

BÉLA BARTÓK
(1881–1945)

A boisterous Hungarian drinking song with a heavily accented melody.

CANON

For Children – book II, no 29

BÉLA BARTÓK
(1881–1945)

Listen for the canonic imitation of the trumpet part in the piano accompaniment. The original folk song text is translated: *"Sleep, sleep, I would sleep…"*

JEERING SONG

For Children – book I, no 30

BÉLA BARTÓK
(1881–1945)

'The sun shines into the church (whoopee!), the priest tolls the bell (whoopee!), enters the church to marry the young couple (whoopee!) and the bride can hardly wait to leave the altar! The repeated patterns in the 2/4 bars accompany the shouts of 'Whoopee!' (*'Ihajja, csuhajja!'*) in the original song.

SWINE-HERD'S SONG

For Children – book I, no 37

BÉLA BARTÓK
(1881–1945)

The text of this Hungarian song is translated: *"Swineherd of Csór, what are you cooking?"* *"Pork with cabbage cooked in fat."* *"Make the old man eat it. If he doesn't, hit him on the cheek."*

BULGARIAN RHYTHM

Mikrokosmos – no 113

BÉLA BARTÓK
(1881–1945)

Four-phrase melody with repeated accompaniment figure. 7/8 is a common time signature in traditional Bulgarian music.

Bartók's original metronome mark is shown, but this piece may be played as effectively at a slower tempo as indicated by the additional editorial tempo marking.

STICK DANCE

Romanian Folk Dances – no 1

BÉLA BARTÓK
(1881–1945)

Originally played on two violins, this melody with accompaniment is written in Dorian and Aeolian modes. Bartók wrote that this is a *'young men's solo dance with various figures, the last of which – as a consummation – consists of kicking the room's ceiling.'*

poco allarg

The Boosey & Hawkes BARTÓK EDITION

Also available *for* Trumpet

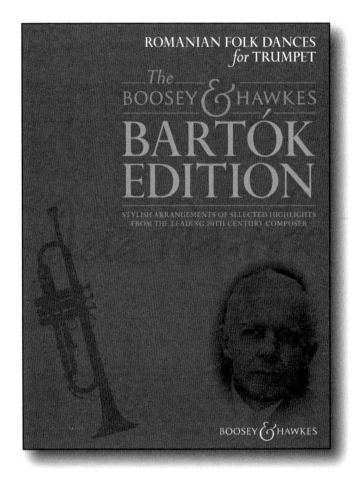

ROMANIAN FOLK DANCES

Suite of six short pieces from 1915
arranged by Hywel Davies for trumpet with piano accompaniment

ISMN 979-0-060-13208-7

BOOSEY & HAWKES

AN IMAGEM COMPANY